G000123971

30 YEARS
OF PRIVATE EYE
CARTOONS

These jokes originally appeared in PRIVATE EYE
Published in Great Britain 1991
by Private Eye Productions Ltd,
6 Carlisle Street, London W1V 5RG

© 1991 Pressdram Ltd
ISBN 1 901784 10 X
Paperback edition reprinted 1991, 1992, 1993, 1997 and 1999
Hardback edition reprinted 1993

Designed by Bridget Tisdall
Printed in Great Britain by Ebenezer Baylis & Son Ltd, Worcester

30 YEARS
OF PRIVATE EYE
CARTOONS

EDITED BY IAN HISLOP

PRIVATE EYE

*"I'm fed up of Poohsticks. Let's go down the arcade
and get ourselves tattooed"*

THE 1960's

*"Adults you are, consenting you may well be, but I
would question the privacy of Lowndes Square"*

"Nigel, I think we're going to have an abortion"

"... and a little man from the village delivers our vegetables"

"Nothing, Laura. It's just that we thought you'd bought a converted pigsty!"

"We'd all like to be strip club proprietors, Milcroft"

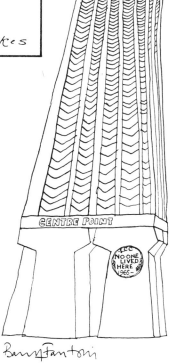

7

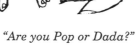

"Are you Pop or Dada?"

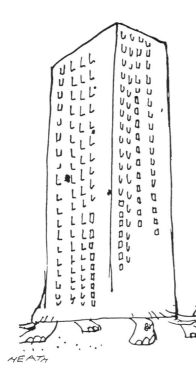

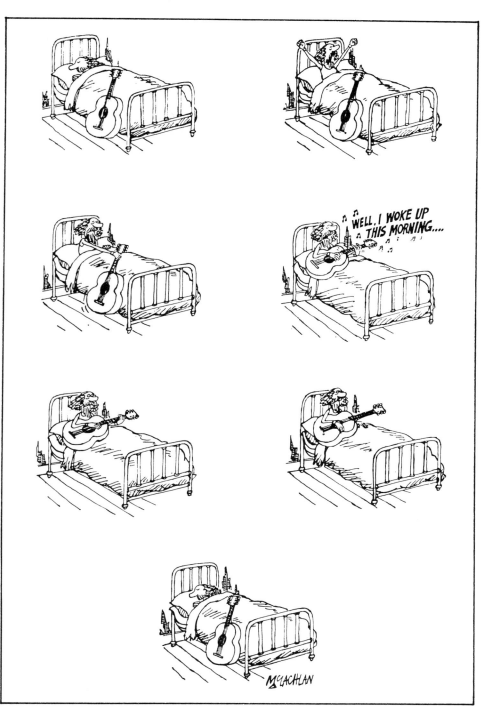

"My wife! Say I'm busy —
in conference, tell her **anything**"

"He's on the couch with
Miss Burnham"

NEW SOCIETY

PARENTS

CHANGING THE COURSE
OF HISTORY

A MIND BLOWING
EXPERIENCE

HEATH

HERO

A HATRED OF CONFORMITY

SOPHISTICATION

A BREAKTHROUGH IN SOUND

A MEANINGFUL RELATIONSHIP

"Are you gay too?"

"Does this damned thing
have a reverse?"

"Clockwise, Knucklehead!"

"Look, I know we used you in our programme on Loneliness three weeks ago, but don't you think you'd better go home to your bed-sit now?"

"Gentlemen, gentlemen! Disorder, please, disorder!"

"Stay! The night is young
and you are enormous"

"All right, I'll go over the strategy just
once more: Get in There and Smash
His Face to a Pulp"

"Sorry, Adults only"

"How dare you talk like that to the woman I'm shacking up with"

"That money wrapped up in a five pound note — it's **mine**! All mine!"

"Tomorrow will be in the low seventies with scattered showers"

HEATH

SPECIAL PECULIARITIES SIR, A MOLE ON THE HEAD?

GREAT POWERS!

WASH & BRUSH UP
2'-

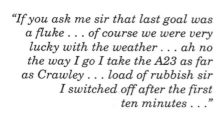

"If you ask me sir that last goal was a fluke . . . of course we were very lucky with the weather . . . ah no the way I go I take the A23 as far as Crawley . . . load of rubbish sir I switched off after the first ten minutes . . ."

HECTOR BREEZE

17

"And this is my wife Media"

*"And now the BBC takes a long cool look at the scandal of
overmanning and restrictive practices in British Industry"*

*"God has also chosen me to speak
to you about insurance"*

"You're taking a chance,
aren't you?"

"Of course you're depressed.
I'm very expensive"

"Look here, Hugget, the Committee would like to know why you're not wearing a club moustache"

*"It was . . .
AAAAAAAGGGGGGGHHHHH . . ."*

*"George Herbert
AAAAAAAGGGGGGGHHHHH?
We have reason to believe . . ."*

Oh! I'm terribly sorry — I mistook you for my husband"

"Come on in, the waiter's lovely"

"My God. It's Hell out there!"

"Guess who's begatting!"

"If the police start asking questions I shall just say that
you packed your things one night and left me"

"Great Heavens!
A Roaring Poof!"

THE
1970's

The Man Who Admitted He Hadn't Been To Bed With Lady Antonia Fraser

"I'm all for cleaning up television, Miss Whitby, but let's keep life filthy!"

"Will you please take your feet
off my best chair!"

"By God, Hornpipe, I wouldn't like to be
a nudist on a night like this"

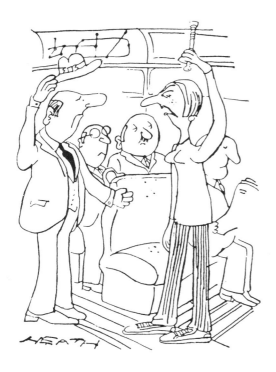

"You bastard!"

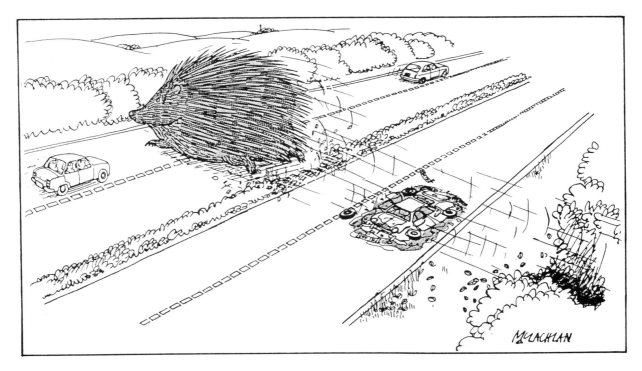

"Read the bit again where I
disinherit the whole family"

Ken Pyne

"I'm campaigning for Greater Personal Privacy.
I wonder if I could come in a minute"

"You're not having any more sweets until
you go and put your teeth in"

"I know they said don't call them, they'd call you, but that was 30 years ago"

"Er . . . mind if we swear?"

"That's what the ploughman has for lunch, fish fingers and chips"

"We call her Melody. She lingers on"

"Does anybody know whether they're supposed to do that?"

"Her ladyship's dead, then"

"GRATE!"

"I've decided to go forth and multiply — !"

31

"I told you never to ring me
at the office!"

"You know what they say. You can never get enough of the stuff"

"When I was a boy we had to make our own entertainment"

GUILTY M'LUD

"I've got this fantastic idea for an idea, man"

"I wish you'd use the nutcrackers, dear"

*"Aye, strange things
can happen at sea"*

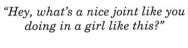

*"Hey, what's a nice joint like you
doing in a girl like this?"*

"He loves to dramatise things"

Congratulations, Mrs. Ravensmoor, you've got a dead husband...

"Gad, I could do with an Eskimo woman right now!"

"You'll like this, sir. It'll make you
both very drunk"

"I'm always rude to black bus
conductors in case they think
I'm a patronizing white liberal"

"Yeah, I'll let you know"

"I still say there's a public footpath through here"

"I still say she's too young to get married"

"Mrs Grimshaw? Here's your dichlor hihig 50-s"

"In bed he just lies there"

"I still think we would have been better off using native porters"

"I loved your single, man"

"Er . . . plus VAT, sir"

"We had sex today"

"Why, Mr Faberge, you've surpassed yourself!"

"Yes we can extend your overdraft but first I'd like a little more grovelling from you please"

"I presume you're aware that Eskimo Nell has had rather a chequered past . . .?"

"Basically I like it, but take out the carrot"

"Looks like we're in
Beatrix Potter country"

"Watch out Glenda, here come
some of those awful gypsies"

"Who wants to carve?"

"You must find it a terrible strain being funny day after day"

"One mouse making it to the top doesn't mean we've got equality"

"And if you fixed the roof you wouldn't have to stay in every time it rained"

"We need a shorter banner
or another member"

"This is his answering service"

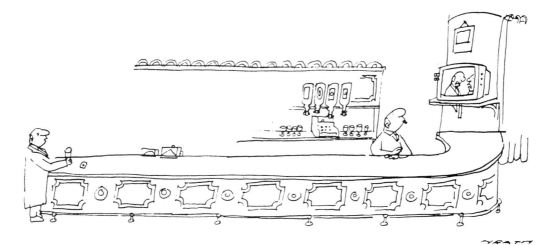

"When the commercials come on could I have half of bitter?"

"It's a start brother. It's a start"

"Good Lord, Fenton, I had no idea you had died!"

"It's from Jane. She's living in sin with someone called Tarzan!"

"Why don't you ever dress up as Albert Schweitzer?"

"Good luck, Minister — and when you lie remember to look straight into the cameras!"

"These are fine, I'll take these"

"The corporal here's got this great idea for a sequel!"

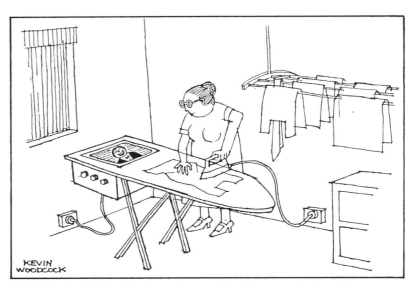

"Sorry to drag you out like this, Doctor"

"Old Smithers hasn't changed much, has he?"

PLUG THIS IN. I'M GONNA SING YOU A CAROL

"These days a popular crop rotation is barley, turnips, pop festival, wheat . . ."

"You can turn the telly on all by yourself now, can't you, Kevin?"

"Don't mind me, I'm from the Bayeux Tapestry"

"Kevin's just killed his first policeman"

"Go on boy, rabbits, go get 'em!"

"Ready? They're coming"

"What a country! Even the dogs are going to the dogs"

SUPER.... SUPER.... WONDERFUL....

LOVELY.... GREAT....

SUPER.... BLESS YOU.... BYE....

BASTARD!

"Tell me, dear, exactly who is this actress Connie Lingus about whom one hears so much these days?"

"Dumbkopf"

50

"I'm a singing letter bomb"

"Oh, look, mother, it's Mabel's special —
alphabet noodle soup"

"Dammit Simpson, this is the third time you've let the tortoise escape"

"60 — 70 — 80 — Phew, what a scorcher!"

"That's the cooker, deepfreeze, washing machine, spin-drier, dish washer and husband"

"Don't colour the whole thing red, Purdy.
Just sizeable chunks"

"Bugger off — I'm considering
the lilies of the field!"

"Here they come!"

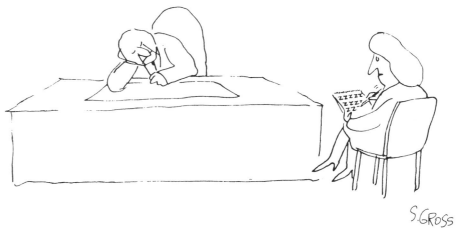

THE
1980's
& ONWARDS

"I must dash — I'm having a coronary at 3.30!"

"Hi! I'm William Fairbrother.
My friends call me Fat Bastard"

"Take an epistle to the Thessalonians, Miss Jones"

"What does it say to you?"

"It's remarkable what modern
surgery can do!"

"Excuse me. Is this the environment?"

"Couldn't you read the paper in the morning
like other husbands?"

"Of course, I'm in private practice now"

"It's all coming back to me now. We were married once, weren't we?"

"Did we tell you about the time we had an overdue library book?"

"All these exposés could make us look very silly indeed"

"Er . . . is that a bid, sir?"

"Well, Trenshaw, this is the last chance for our super-intelligence drug XLR6. I've just given the rat the injection"

"Yet another one dead!! That's it, I guess . . . it doesn't work. Take it away!"

"I wish you'd eat
that doughnut"

"Mouse! . . . What mouse?"

"We'll have the consomme, the lobster
and an extra large portion of
grovelling servility"

"You know what they say, Job. Everyone has a book in him"

"And remember to call in for a vasectomy on your way home"

"I'm just ringing to say I'm ringing from the car!"

GED.

"You patronising bastard!"

"My wife makes the
best dumplings ever"

"They say the first quarrel
is always the worst!"

"And that, m'lud, concludes the case for the prosecution"

"Typical! You wait ages for Godot,
then three come at once!"

"Young Willy's very much like his father, isn't he?"

"Teddy-bears' picnics
aren't what they used
to be"

*"I wish I could pull the birds
like you, Brother Francis"*

"Not this crap again?"

*"Frankly Michael, I think it's possible to take
cosmetic surgery too far"*

"He's changed his mind. He wants to be cremated"

"Well, you did say they should go outside and get some fresh air"

"Mr and Mrs Smith"

"Looks like a case for Mr Sherlock Holmes, Inspector"

"The designer stubble is getting a little out of hand Rasputin"

"It's Mavis. Apparently Jack's
just died, so would we mind
if they leave it tonight?"

"Don't come the Innocent with me"

"Don't worry, there'll be another one along in a minute"

"Then for twenty years he was on Aircraft Carriers"

"It's all changed since Frankenstein went private"

"The new manager is quite a 'go-getter' isn't he?"

"It's a digital dandelion"

"Would you like to come back to my place? I've got three different types of mustard"

"See what I mean Achmed, it's not the deterrent it used to be"

"Never mind the porridge.
She's taken the video"

"Who gives this woman to be hit?"

"I thought you said you'd done this before"

"I swore I'd make him do something useful around the house one day, so I put his ashes in the egg timer"

"It's amazing what Henry finds down behind the sofa cushions"

"Not another bloody sequel!"

"I'll have the steak"

"Let me through — I'm the story after the break"

"Good morning madam —
Jehoover's Witness"

"This will be your room.
They'll ring if they
want anything . . ."

"Don't worry about Moses. He can look after himself"

"It looks like aid, but I think there
are strings attached"

"This hypochondria — can you
give me something for it?"

"Maggie and I have been going
through a bad patch, Ernie"

"It was your chairman's last wish"

"We're playing mothers and fathers and he's got access to my doll at weekends"

"I won't have you cluttering up the room with your things!!"

"I wouldn't mind but these are only the popadums"

*"Well, we haven't made a very good
start have we, Mrs Turnstone?"*

*"It seems to reach exactly the same
part as all other lagers"*

"Apparently they're friends of your fathers from the golf club"

"Oh no! The Cow's burning up on re-entry!"

"Oh yes, we can change your spots. It's quite an operation, but we can do it"

"Gye, gye, cruel world!"

"Hello Bill.
How's the wife?"

"It's desperate, sir — we're down to our last poet!"

"Shall I be mother figure?"

"OK, sergeant, Scotland Yard'll handle it now —
where exactly was the body found?"

"Capitalist Bastard, Capitalist Bastard . . ."

"Well, I think we made a very good impression on the candidates — !"

"I'd like you to meet the rest of the family"

"Anything to get out for a pint"

"He's a disgrace to lemmings!"

"Call my wife a tramp, would you Batley?"

*"Don't be too critical
of the lad, George"*

"How many ants do you want?"

"Oh no! Synchronised Ladies of the Lake!"

"I'm sorry, Hodger. Having worms is no excuse for
these very poor sales figures"

"Don't worry Mrs Dumpty — we're doing everything
we can to talk your son out of it . . ."

"Denis is trying to grow a beard"

"I'm rounding up stray supermarket trolleys"

"Come back! I was just getting ready!"

"Not while I'm on duty, sir"

"Dear Mum, I've found a friend"

"It's the most sophisticated camera in the world,
but I can't find anything worth photographing"

*"Well I don't call it heaven when we're not
allowed to sniff each other's bottoms"*

*"Good afternoon — we're recruitment consultants
for His Majesty's Navy"*

"This IS a theme pub — the theme is getting drunk!"

"Our tap's been phoned!"

"This is Mr Trimp from the Town and Country Planning Department. He's here to demonstrate the proposals for the old town"

"He's slow but he's good"

"They insist that we accept a gay couple"

"Sorry, didn't we tell you? We changed it to best out of three . . ."

"You'll have to excuse my husband, he's an alcoholic"

"Take a card, any card"

"There, what am I always telling you —
young people today are soft!"

"This is the worst part of the job — having to clear up after a Rugby International"

"Look out! It's a vicious circle!"

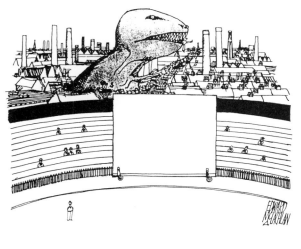

"... And once again we have interruption of play caused by movement behind the bowler's arm ..."

*"Excuse me,
is this
Alcoholics
Hieronymous?"*

"Can I borrow your wig tonight, Dad?"

*"You're ruthless, Collins. I like
that in a manager"*

"Not for me, thank you — it keeps me awake all afternoon"

"Go on! What is he — police car, fire engine or ambulance?"

"We can do without your down to earth realism, Henshaw"

"I'd like to know who keeps sending us these bloody silly Norman Tebbitgrams!"

"I'm afraid he's got Odes, Mrs Keats"

"Has he been watching video nasties again?"

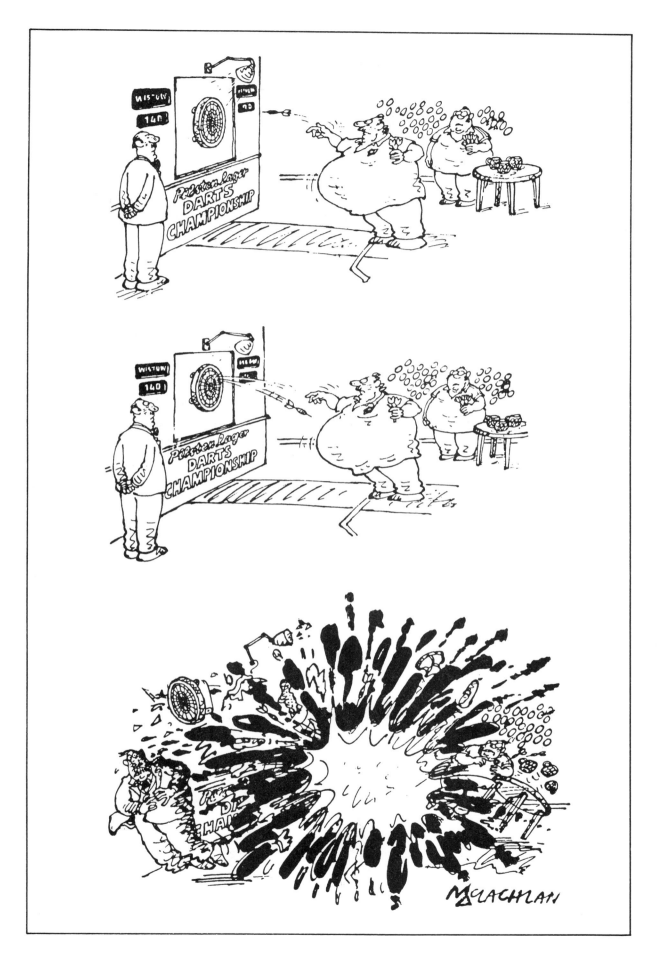

Other Private Eye Books

ON SALE NOW

THE PRIVATE EYE ANNUAL

ST ALBION PARISH NEWS

and the

COLEMANBALLS
series